Contents

AGES 6–7
KEY STAGE 1

Premier

MATHS

Numbers to 20

The numbers between 12 and 20 are **teen** numbers.

They all end in **...teen**.

11 and 12 are made from a ten and ones, but do not end in **teen**.

> 13 → thirteen
>
> 10 + 3 = 13

I) Write the words or numbers for each of these.

a   15 →

b   18 →

c   11 →

d   17 →

e   fourteen →

f   nineteen →

g   twelve →

h   sixteen →

II) Write the word for each number.

a 13 →

b 12 →

c 18 →

d 17 →

e 14 →

f 19 →

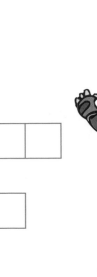

The hidden number in the shaded area is ⬚ .

Counting

Use this grid to help you learn the **order** of numbers to 50.

1	2	3	4	5	6	7	8	9	10
11	12	13	14	15	16	17	18	19	20
21	22	23	24	25	26	27	28	29	30
31	32	33	34	35	36	37	38	39	40
41	42	43	44	45	46	47	48	49	50

I Fill in the missing numbers.

a 27 28 ☐ ☐ ☐ 32 ☐ 34 ☐ ☐

b ☐ ☐ ☐ 43 44 ☐ ☐ ☐ 48 49

c ☐ ☐ 29 ☐ 27 26 ☐ ☐ 23 22

d ☐ ☐ 48 ☐ ☐ 45 44 43 ☐ ☐

e 16 ☐ ☐ ☐ 20 ☐ 22 ☐ 24 ☐

II These are all part of the 1–50 grid. Use the grid at the top of the page to help fill in the missing numbers.

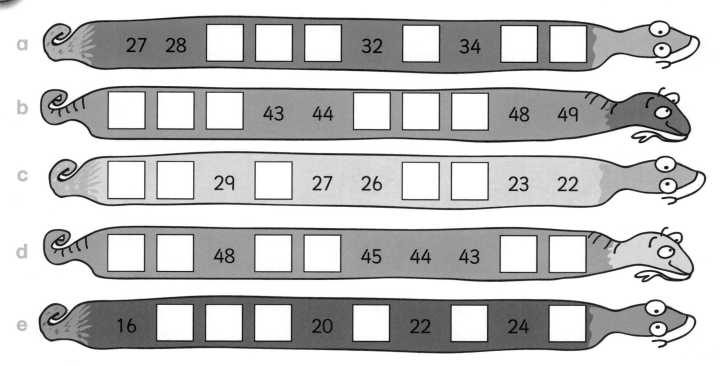

a
	☐		
14		☐	
	26	28	☐
35			

b
22		☐	
32	33		36
		44	

c
			10
		18	
		38	40

3

Adding

A **number line** can help with addition.

What is 4 + 7?

Start with the biggest number and count on.

7 + 4 = 11

I Use the number line to help add these pairs of numbers.

a 6 3 → ☐   e 6 6 → ☐   i 3 8 → ☐

b 5 7 → ☐   f 9 5 → ☐   j 6 7 → ☐

c 8 4 → ☐   g 4 9 → ☐   k 8 5 → ☐

d 7 2 → ☐   h 7 8 → ☐   l 7 7 → ☐

II Draw a line from each addition problem to its total. Colour the star with no matching fact.

a 3 + 9

c 7 + 7

e 8 + 8

g 7 + 3

i 10 + 9

f 7 + 6

b 9 + 9

d 9 + 6

j 6 + 5

h 10 + 10

10 11 12 13 14 15 16 17 18 19 20

2-D shapes

A 2-D shape is a **flat shape**.

Learn the names and number of sides of these shapes.

| triangle | quadrilateral | pentagon | hexagon | heptagon | octagon |
| 3 sides | 4 sides | 5 sides | 6 sides | 7 sides | 8 sides |

Rectangles and squares are special quadrilaterals.

Draw lines to join the shapes to the correct name.

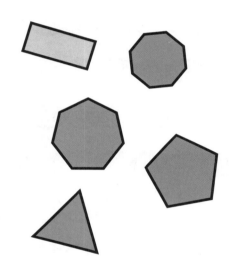

triangle

rectangle

pentagon

hexagon

heptagon

octagon

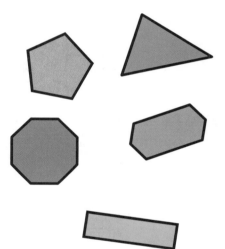

Colour this stained glass window using the colour code below.

 triangles

 quadrilaterals

 pentagons

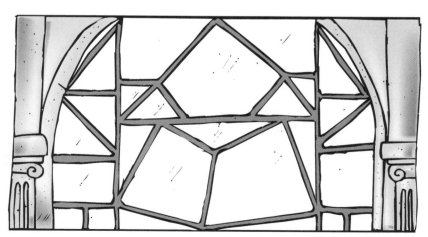

5

Taking away

You can count back along a number line to help you **subtract**, or **take away**.

What is 14 – 5? Start at 14 and count back 5.

0 1 2 3 4 5 6 7 8 9 10 11 12 13 14 15

14 – 5 = 9

I Show the jumps for each subtraction. Then write the answer in the box.

a 11 – 4 = ☐   1 2 3 4 5 6 7 8 9 10 11 12 13 14 15

b 13 – 5 = ☐   1 2 3 4 5 6 7 8 9 10 11 12 13 14 15

c 12 – 7 = ☐   1 2 3 4 5 6 7 8 9 10 11 12 13 14 15

d 16 – 7 = ☐   6 7 8 9 10 11 12 13 14 15 16 17 18 19 20

e 18 – 6 = ☐   6 7 8 9 10 11 12 13 14 15 16 17 18 19 20

f 17 – 6 = ☐   6 7 8 9 10 11 12 13 14 15 16 17 18 19 20

II Make each subtraction match the number on the stars.

a

10 – ☐

☐ – 2

6

12 – ☐

☐ – 3

☐ – 8

b

11 – ☐

☐ – 7

7

9 – ☐

☐ – 6

15 – ☐

6

Numbers to *100*

This grid shows the numbers to 100.

Use the **tens** to help you read and write the numbers.

20 twenty	60 sixty
30 thirty	70 seventy
40 forty	80 eighty
50 fifty	90 ninety

1	2	3	4	5	6	7	8	9	10
11	12	13	14	15	16	17	18	19	20
21	22	23	24	25	26	27	28	29	30
31	32	33	34	35	36	37	38	39	40
41	42	43	44	45	46	47	48	49	50
51	52	53	54	55	56	57	58	59	60
61	62	63	64	65	66	67	68	69	70
71	72	73	74	75	76	77	78	79	80
81	82	83	84	85	86	87	88	89	90
91	92	93	94	95	96	97	98	99	100

1 Circle the correct number for each of these.

a thirty-eight   83   37   78   38   30

b fifty-four   44   50   46   45   54

c seventy-nine   97   17   79   76   96

d sixty-two   52   26   60   62   80

e eighty-seven   81   78   80   76   87

2 Find these numbers on the word search. They are written across → and down ↓.

20	60
30	70
40	80
50	90

T	W	E	N	T	Y	E	F
N	S	I	X	T	Y	F	I
I	Y	G	N	H	V	O	F
N	E	H	E	Y	I	R	T
E	S	T	H	I	R	T	Y
T	R	Y	M	L	F	Y	E
Y	S	E	V	E	N	T	Y

Addition and subtraction

This **number trio** can make 4 addition and subtraction facts.

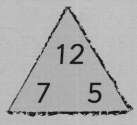

$$7 + 5 = 12 \qquad 12 - 7 = 5$$
$$5 + 7 = 12 \qquad 12 - 5 = 7$$

 Fill in the addition and subtraction facts for these.

a

| 5 | + | ☐ | = | ☐ |

☐ + 5 = ☐

☐ − 5 = ☐

☐ − ☐ = 5

b

☐ + ☐ = 15

☐ + 6 = 15

15 − ☐ = ☐

15 − ☐ = ☐

c

9 + ☐ = ☐

☐ + 9 = ☐

☐ − ☐ = 9

☐ − 9 = ☐

 Choose 8 different numbers from the line below to complete these facts.

4 + ☐ = 9   7 − 5 = ☐   8 − ☐ = 1

☐ + ☐ = 11   12 − ☐ = 8   ☐ + 3 = ☐

8

Counting patterns

Practise **counting on** and **back** in steps of 2, 5 and 10.

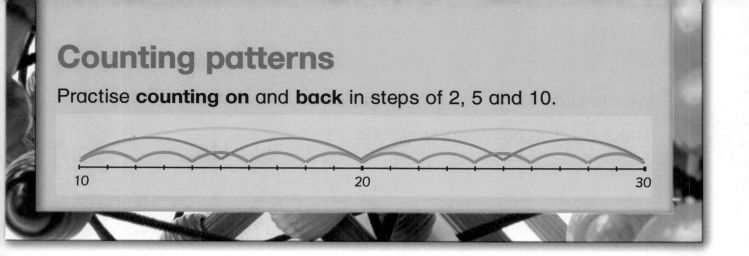

I Continue each of these counting patterns to 100. Mark them on the 100 square like this:

2 4 6 8 10 12 → 100

5 10 15 20 25 → 100

10 20 30 40 50 → 100

1	2	3	4	5	6	7	8	9	10
11	12	13	14	15	16	17	18	19	20
21	22	23	24	25	26	27	28	29	30
31	32	33	34	35	36	37	38	39	40
41	42	43	44	45	46	47	48	49	50
51	52	53	54	55	56	57	58	59	60
61	62	63	64	65	66	67	68	69	70
71	72	73	74	75	76	77	78	79	80
81	82	83	84	85	86	87	88	89	90
91	92	93	94	95	96	97	98	99	100

II Count in 5s and fill in the next 4 numbers.

a

b

c

Now count in 10s and fill in the next 4 numbers.

d

e

f

Measuring length

We measure lengths using **centimetres** and **metres**.

There are 100 centimetres (cm) in 1 metre (m).

100 cm = 1 m

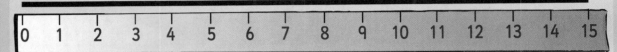

This line shows 15 cm.

I Use a ruler to measure each of these lengths in centimetres.

a _____ ⬜ cm

b _____ ⬜ cm

c _____ ⬜ cm

d ___ ⬜ cm

e _____ ⬜ cm

f _____ ⬜ cm

> Try estimating the length before you measure.

II Draw lines to join these objects to the most likely length.

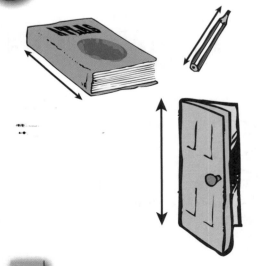

about 1 metre

about 2 metres

about 10 centimetres

more than 2 metres

about 50 cm

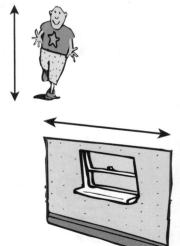

Finding totals

When you add together 3 or more numbers, try **starting** with the **largest number**.

Here's how to total 4, 3 and 8:

$$8 + 4 = 12$$
$$12 + 3 = 15$$

You could look for pairs that are easy to total.

Here's how to total 6, 5 and 4:

$$6 + 4 = 10$$
$$10 + 5 = 15$$

I Fill in the totals for these sets of additions.

a 6 2 8 → ☐

b 5 2 9 → ☐

c 7 2 3 → ☐

d 9 1 8 → ☐

e 7 3 4 → ☐

f 5 9 5 → ☐

g 8 4 6 → ☐

h 3 3 8 → ☐

i 4 6 3 → ☐

II Make these totals in different ways.

a

4 + ☐ + ☐

☐ + ☐ + 5

☐ + 6 + ☐

13

☐ + 3 + ☐

8 + ☐ + ☐

☐ + ☐ + 1

b

☐ + ☐ + 9

☐ + 6 + ☐

7 + ☐ + ☐

18

4 + ☐ + ☐

☐ + 8 + ☐

☐ + ☐ + 5

Odd and even numbers

Even numbers always end in

2 4 6 8 0

36
is an even number.

Odd numbers always end in

1 3 5 7 9

63
is an odd number.

I **Write the next even number.**

a 22 → ☐

b 38 → ☐

c 46 → ☐

d 60 → ☐

e 54 → ☐

Write the next odd number.

f 35 → ☐

g 57 → ☐

h 29 → ☐

i 87 → ☐

j 91 → ☐

II **Colour red the even number trail. Start at the IN gate.**

OUT

19	24	32	48	85	33	34	26	18	70	96	73	34	26	14
23	6	61	16	51	27	58	35	43	19	34	85	58	21	43
42	30	25	40	10	7	94	65	24	46	52	17	92	80	19
85	27	41	93	28	43	62	97	12	21	33	29	31	52	21
17	35	43	8	32	76	44	81	16	54	36	28	56	74	45

IN

How many stars have you collected? ☐

12

3-D shapes

A 3-D shape is a **solid shape**.

Learn the names of these shapes. Look at the faces.

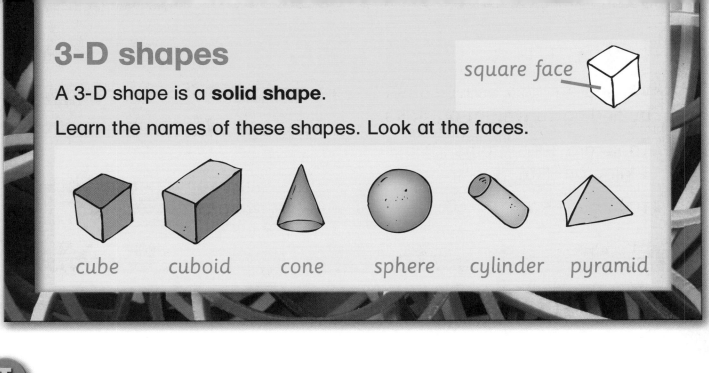

square face

cube   cuboid   cone   sphere   cylinder   pyramid

I Draw lines to join each shape to its correct name.

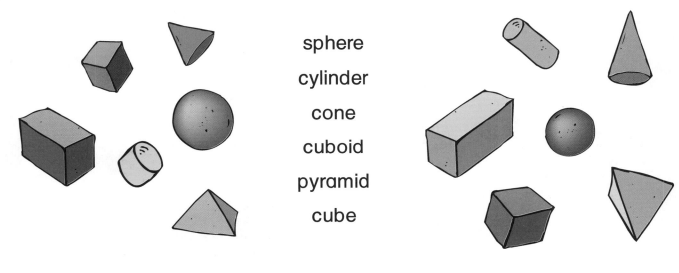

sphere

cylinder

cone

cuboid

pyramid

cube

II Fill in the number of faces for each of these shapes.

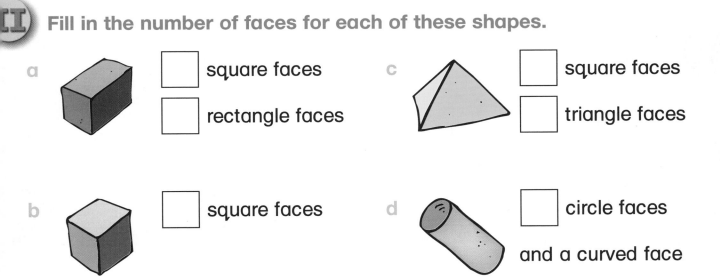

a   ☐ square faces
     ☐ rectangle faces

c   ☐ square faces
     ☐ triangle faces

b   ☐ square faces

d   ☐ circle faces
     and a curved face

Measuring mass

We find out how heavy something is by finding its **weight** or **mass**.

There are 1000 grams (g) in 1 kilogram (kg).

1000 g = 1 kg

Find something that weighs about 1 kg.

I Join these to the most likely weight.

II Write down the weight on the scales to the nearest kilogram.

a   b   c   d

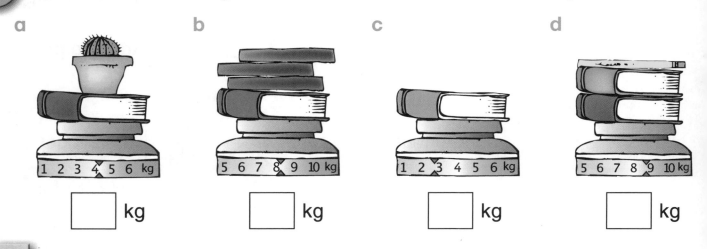

☐ kg   ☐ kg   ☐ kg   ☐ kg

Breaking up numbers

The numbers between **10** and **99** all have **two digits**.

57 → 50 + 7

5 tens   7 ones

I Fill in the missing numbers.

a 34 → 30 + ☐

b 51 → ☐ + 1

c 47 → 40 + ☐

d 65 → ☐ + 5

e 83 → 80 + ☐

f 42 → ☐ + 2

g 29 → 20 + ☐

h 76 → ☐ + 6

i 59 → 50 + ☐

II Draw lines to join the matching pairs.

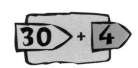

Reading the time

These clocks show **quarter past eight**.

8:15

15 minutes have gone past 8 o'clock.

These clocks show **quarter to five**.

4:45

45 minutes have gone past 4 o'clock.

 **I** Draw lines to join the clocks showing the same time.

a   b   c   d   e   f   g

| 11:30 | 3:00 | 1:15 | 12:45 | 6:45 | 4:15 | 7:15 |

 II Write the number of minutes between each of these times.

a  ☐ minutes

c **10:45** **11:00** ☐ minutes

b  ☐ minutes

d **3:15** **3:45** ☐ minutes

16

$5 + 5 =$

Answer: 10

$5 + 7 =$

Answer: 12

$9 + 5 =$

Answer: 14

$6 +$  $= 9$

Answer: 3

$3 +$ $= 11$

Answer: 8

$3 +$ $= 13$

Answer: 10

 $+ 4 = 8$

Answer: 4

$+ 4 = 12$

Answer: 8

 $+ 9 = 12$

Answer: 3

$$8 - 4 = \text{☁}$$

Answer: 12

$$\text{☁} - 1 = 5$$

Answer: 6

$$\text{☁} - 3 = 4$$

Answer: 7

$$\text{☁} - 7 = 6$$

Answer: 2

$$\text{☁} - 9 = 2$$

Answer: 4

$$\text{☁} - 5 = 2$$

Answer: 3

$$9 - 5 = \text{☁}$$

Answer: 1

$$8 - 3 = \text{☁}$$

Answer: 5

$$6 - 3 = \text{☁}$$

Answer: 3

9 − 4 = 3

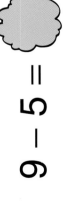

Answer: **7**

12 − 7 = 1

Answer: **8**

13 − 9 = 3

Answer: **12**

10 − ☁ = 5

Answer: **5**

8 − ☁ = 3

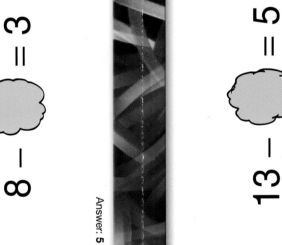

Answer: **5**

13 − ☁ = 5

Answer: **8**

9 − 5 = ☁

Answer: **4**

10 − 7 = ☁

Answer: **3**

11 − 4 = ☁

Answer: **7**

$3 + 3 =$

Answer: 6

$5 + 3 =$

Answer: 8

$7 + 3 =$

Answer: 10

$4 +$  $= 6$

Answer: 2

$6 +$ $= 7$

Answer: 1

$4 +$  $= 7$

Answer: 3

 $+ 2 = 5$

Answer: 3

$+ 1 = 3$

Answer: 2

$+ 2 = 8$

Answer: 6

Multiplying

Counting in equal groups is also called **multiplying**.

The multiplication sign is ×.

3 + 3 + 3 + 3 = 12

4 lots of 3 is 12

4 × 3 = 12

4 + 4 + 4 = 12

3 lots of 4 is 12

3 × 4 = 12

These both give the same answer.

Write the answers to these facts.

a  2 + 2 + 2 = ☐

3 × 2 = ☐

d  4 + 4 = ☐

2 × 4 = ☐

b  5 + 5 = ☐

2 × 5 = ☐

e   3 + 3 + 3 = ☐

3 × 3 = ☐

c   3 + 3 + 3 + 3 + 3 = ☐

5 × 3 = ☐

f   4 + 4 + 4 + 4 = ☐

4 × 4 = ☐

Draw 2 spots on each hat. Then write the answer.

a

6 × 2 = ☐

Draw 3 spots on each hat. Then write the answer.

b

6 × 3 = ☐

Symmetrical shapes

Shapes are **symmetrical** if they are the same either side of a **mirror line**.

The mirror line is called the **line of symmetry**.

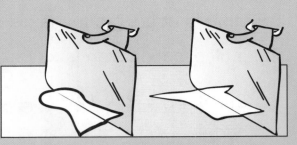

I Draw a line of symmetry on each of these shapes.

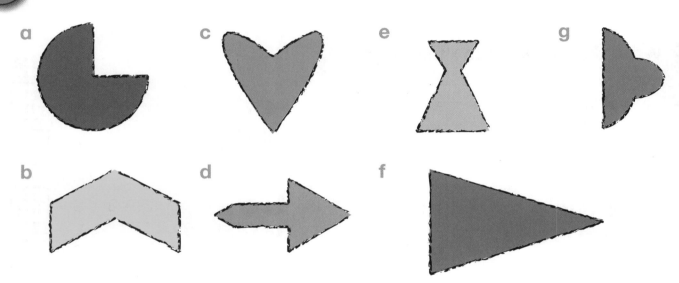

a

b

c

d

e

f

g

II Complete this to make a symmetrical shape. Then colour it to make a symmetrical pattern.

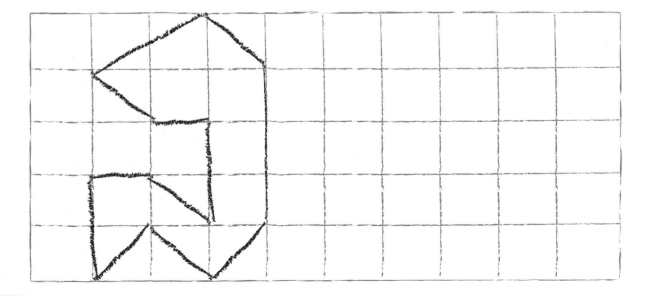

Ordering numbers

When you put **2-digit** numbers in order, look at the **tens and then the ones** digit.

Use this number line to help.

52 is larger than 38 because 5 tens is more than 3 tens.

Write a number in each box so there are four numbers in order.

a [42] [ ] [ ] [50] d [82] [ ] [ ] [91] g [94] [ ] [ ] [98]

b [61] [ ] [ ] [73] e [66] [ ] [ ] [71] h [88] [ ] [ ] [92]

c [57] [ ] [ ] [64] f [76] [ ] [ ] [83] i [57] [ ] [ ] [61]

Write these sets in order, starting with the smallest amount.

a

58p 39p 85p 61p 42p

[ ]p [ ]p [ ]p [ ]p [ ]p

b
73 kg 69 kg 37 kg 39 kg 76 kg

[ ] kg [ ] kg [ ] kg [ ] kg [ ] kg

c

32 cm 23 cm 80 cm 38 cm 28 cm

[ ] cm [ ] cm [ ] cm [ ] cm [ ] cm

d
£53 £62 £29 £65 £35

£[ ] £[ ] £[ ] £[ ] £[ ]

19

Dividing

Dividing a number of objects can be shown by grouping them.

The division sign is ÷.

6 beans grouped in twos, gives 3 groups

$6 \div 2 = 3$

 Draw loops around these beans to group them. Write the answers.

a 8 grouped in 2s

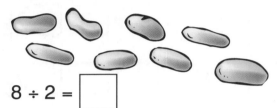

$8 \div 2 = \boxed{}$

c 12 grouped in 3s

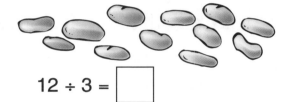

$12 \div 3 = \boxed{}$

b 9 grouped in 3s

$9 \div 3 = \boxed{}$

d 10 grouped in 2s

$10 \div 2 = \boxed{}$

 Use the cookies to help you complete these.

a

$15 \div 5 = \boxed{}$

c

$10 \div 2 = \boxed{}$

b

$15 \div 3 = \boxed{}$

d

$10 \div 5 = \boxed{}$

Reading graphs

Block graphs show information in a simple way.

Count the blocks carefully or read across for the amount.

A group of children threw 10 beanbags trying to get them into a bucket.

How many more beanbags did Zoe get in than Fred?

I A group of children tested how many pegs they could hold in one hand.

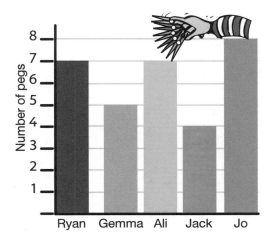

a Who held the most pegs?

b How many pegs did Gemma hold?

c Which 2 children held the same number of pegs?

d Who held the fewest pegs?

e How many more pegs did Jo hold than Jack?

I Carry out your own peg test. Ask family and friends to hold as many pegs as they can in one hand. Record your results as a pictogram.

Name	Number of pegs

= 1 peg

Time

There are **12 months** or **52 weeks** in **a year**.

Try to learn the order of the months and the seasons. Think about the month and season you were born in.

 spring summer autumn winter

I Complete the names of the months for each season.

spring

M __ __ c h

A __ r __ l

__ __ y

winter

D __ __ __ m b __ __

__ __ n u __ r __

F __ __ r __ __ __ y

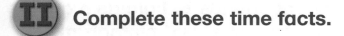

summer

J __ __ e

__ __ __ y

A __ __ u __ __

autumn

S __ p __ __ __ __ __ r

__ __ t __ b __ __

N __ __ e __ b __ __

II Complete these time facts.

a ▢ days in a week

b ▢ months in a year

c ▢ weeks in a year

d ▢ hours in a day

e ▢ minutes in an hour

f ▢ seconds in a minute

g ▢ days in a fortnight

h ▢ days in a weekend

i ▢ seasons in a year

j ▢ months in a season

2 times table

The numbers in the **2 times table** can be shown as a pattern.

Try to learn the 2 times table by heart.

$$1 \times 2 = 2$$
$$2 \times 2 = 4$$

Draw lines to join the questions to the correct answers.

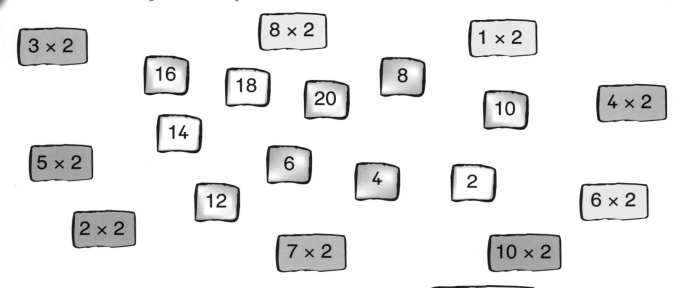

3 × 2   8 × 2   1 × 2

16   18   20   8   10   4 × 2

14

5 × 2   6   4   2   6 × 2

12

2 × 2

7 × 2   10 × 2

a **Write a calculation for the answer that is left.**

Answer these questions as fast as you can. Ask someone to time you.

a 3 × 2 = ☐   b 2 × 10 = ☐   c 8 × 2 = ☐

7 × 2 = ☐   2 × 2 = ☐   2 × 6 = ☐

4 × 2 = ☐   2 × 8 = ☐   9 × 2 = ☐

1 × 2 = ☐   2 × 5 = ☐   2 × 7 = ☐

6 × 2 = ☐   2 × 9 = ☐   5 × 2 = ☐

23

Half fractions

This chocolate bar is cut into **2 equal pieces**.

Each piece is **half ($\frac{1}{2}$)** of the whole bar.

There are 8 squares of chocolate.

$\frac{1}{2}$ of 8 = 4

I Colour $\frac{1}{2}$ of each shape.

a

c

e

b

d

f

II Circle $\frac{1}{2}$ of each set. Write the answer.

a  $\frac{1}{2}$ of 6 = ☐

c  $\frac{1}{2}$ of 10 = ☐

b 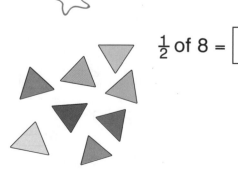 $\frac{1}{2}$ of 8 = ☐

d  $\frac{1}{2}$ of 4 = ☐

24

Measuring capacity

The **capacity** of a jug shows how much **liquid** it holds.

> 1000 millilitres (ml) = 1 litre (l)

Fill a 1 litre jug so that you know how much a litre is.

 Draw lines to join these things to the most likely amount.

| less than 1 litre | greater than 1 litre |

 Write down these amounts to the nearest litre.

a

[ ] litres

c

[ ] litres

e

[ ] litres

b

[ ] litres

d

[ ] litres

f

[ ] litres

25

Money

Practise finding totals of **coins** and giving **change**. When you give change, try counting up.

A cake costs 39p. Think about the change you will get from 50p.

Count on from 39p to 50p.

+1p   +10p

39p   40p   50p

The change is 11p.

I Draw the 3 coins you would use to buy each of these.

a  42p ○○○

d  16p ○○○

b  53p ○○○

e  80p ○○○

c  £1.15 ○○○

f  £1.40 ○○○

II This is the change given from 50p. How much did each cake cost?

a

cost → [ ]p

b

cost → [ ]p

c

cost → [ ]p

26

Number sequences

This sequence counts on in **steps of 2**.

5 6 **7** 8 **9** 10 **11** 12 **13** 14 **15**

The difference between each number is 2.

When you are writing sequences of numbers, look at the **difference** between each number.

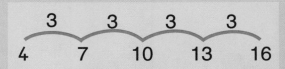

3   3   3   3
4   7   10   13   16

Write the next 2 numbers in each sequence.

a   14   16   18   20   22   ☐   ☐

b   17   20   23   26   29   ☐   ☐

c   27   25   23   21   19   ☐   ☐

d   11   16   21   26   31   ☐   ☐

e   36   32   28   24   20   ☐   ☐

Write 3 sequences of your own. The number 20 must be in each sequence.

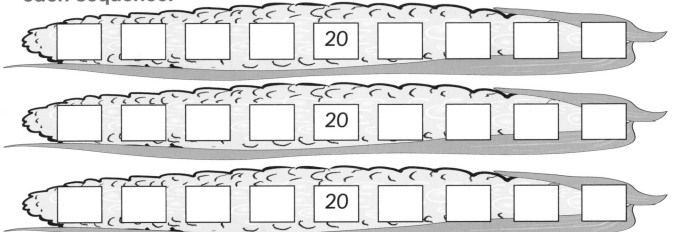

☐ ☐ ☐ ☐ 20 ☐ ☐ ☐ ☐

☐ ☐ ☐ ☐ 20 ☐ ☐ ☐ ☐

☐ ☐ ☐ ☐ 20 ☐ ☐ ☐ ☐

Multiplication facts

Try to learn the **2** times,
5 times and **10** times tables.

Use this grid to help you.

×	1	2	3	4	5	6	7	8	9	10
2	2	4	6	8	10	12	14	16	18	20
5	5	10	15	20	25	30	35	40	45	50
10	10	20	30	40	50	60	70	80	90	100

I Cover the grid above. Now answer these questions as fast as you can. Check your answers, then try to beat your score.

a 3 × 5 = ☐   b 4 × 2 = ☐   c 2 × 2 = ☐   d 5 × 2 = ☐

6 × 2 = ☐   7 × 10 = ☐   9 × 10 = ☐   8 × 10 = ☐

4 × 10 = ☐   9 × 2 = ☐   6 × 5 = ☐   10 × 5 = ☐

8 × 2 = ☐   5 × 5 = ☐   2 × 10 = ☐   3 × 2 = ☐

4 × 5 = ☐   3 × 10 = ☐   7 × 5 = ☐   9 × 5 = ☐

II Write the digits 1 to 9 in the boxes to make each sum correct.

2 × ☐ = ☐   ☐ × 5 = 20   ☐0 × ☐ = 80

☐ × ☐ = 35   ☐ × ☐ = 18

☐ × ☐ = 40

28

Quarter fractions

This cake is cut into **4 equal pieces**.

Each piece is **one quarter ($\frac{1}{4}$)** of the whole cake.

A quarter of 8 is 2

$\frac{1}{4}$ of 8 = 2

1 Colour $\frac{1}{4}$ of each shape.

a

c

e

b

d

f

2 Colour $\frac{1}{4}$ of the ribbons on these badges. Make sure each pattern is different.

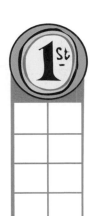

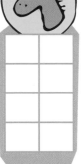

Problems

Read word problems carefully. Look for **key words** to help you.

| add, total, sum, altogether, plus, increase | subtract, take away, difference, fewer, decrease | times, multiply, lots of, double, groups of | share, divide, group, halve |

I Answer these problems.

a Four friends share 20 pencils equally between them. How many pencils do they each have?

b A T-shirt costs £3.50. What change will there be from £5?

c Tom buys 2 boxes of eggs with 6 eggs in each. When he gets home he finds that 3 eggs are cracked. How many eggs are not cracked?

d When a tree was planted, it was 2 metres high. After 5 years it was 10 times as high. What height was it after 5 years?

e Entrance to a fête costs 40p for adults and 10p for children. What is the total cost for a family of 2 adults and 3 children?

II Answer these 'think of a number' puzzles.

a I think of a number and then add 2. The answer is 7. What was my number?

b I think of a number and then take away 5. The answer is 6. What was my number?

c I think of a number and then halve it. The answer is 4. What was my number?

d I think of a number and then double it. The answer is 10. What was my number?

Finding the difference

To find the **difference** between 2 numbers, count on from the smaller number.

What is the difference between 19 and 23?

19 20 21 22 23 24 25   23 − 19 = 4

Write the difference in price between these pairs of items.

a

Difference: £ [ ]

c

Difference: £ [ ]

e

Difference: £ [ ]

b

Difference: £ [ ]

d

Difference: £ [ ]

f

Difference: £ [ ]

Draw lines to join pairs with a difference of 6.

ANSWERS

Page 2

I
- **a** fifteen
- **b** eighteen
- **c** eleven
- **d** seventeen
- **e** 14
- **f** 19
- **g** 12
- **h** 16

II
- **a** thirteen
- **b** twelve
- **c** eighteen
- **d** seventeen
- **e** fourteen
- **f** nineteen

The hidden number is 11

Page 3

I
- **a** 29, 30, 31, 33, 35, 36
- **b** 40, 41, 42, 45, 46, 47
- **c** 31, 30, 28, 25, 24
- **d** 50, 49, 47, 46, 42, 41
- **e** 17, 18, 19, 21, 23, 25

II a

	5				
14	15		17		
24	25	26	27	28	29
	35	36	37	38	
	45	46			

b

22	23		25	26
32	33	34	35	36
42		44	45	

c

6	7	8		10
		18	19	20
		28	29	30
	37	38	39	40
			49	50

Page 4

I
- **a** 9
- **b** 12
- **c** 12
- **d** 9
- **e** 12
- **f** 14
- **g** 13
- **h** 15
- **i** 11
- **j** 13
- **k** 13
- **l** 14

II
- **a** 12
- **b** 18
- **c** 14
- **d** 15
- **e** 16
- **f** 13
- **g** 10
- **h** 20
- **i** 19
- **j** 11

17 is the star coloured in.

Page 5

I

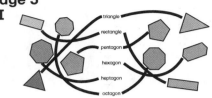

II Check your child's colouring is accurate.

Page 6

I
- **a** 7
- **b** 8
- **c** 5
- **d** 9
- **e** 12
- **f** 11

II
- **a** 8 – 2, 10 – 4, 12 – 6, 14 – 8, 9 – 3
- **b** 14 – 7, 11 – 4, 9 – 2, 15 – 8, 13 – 6

Page 7

I
- **a** 38
- **b** 54
- **c** 79
- **d** 62
- **e** 87

II

T	W	E	N	T	Y	E	F
N	S	I	X	T	Y	F	I
I	Y	G	N	H	V	O	F
N	E	H	E	Y	I	R	T
E	S	T	H	I	R	T	Y
T	R	Y	M	L	F	Y	E
Y	S	E	V	E	N	T	Y

Page 8

I
- **a** 5 + 8 = 13
  8 + 5 = 13
  13 – 5 = 8
  13 – 8 = 5
- **b** 6 + 9 = 15
  9 + 6 = 15
  15 – 9 = 6
  15 – 6 = 9
- **c** 9 + 8 = 17
  8 + 9 = 17
  17 – 8 = 9
  17 – 9 = 8

II 4 + 5 = 9   12 – 4 = 8
8 + 3 = 11   8 – 7 = 1
7 – 5 = 2   6 + 3 = 9

Page 9

I

1	2	3	4	5	6	7	8	9	10
11	12	13	14	15	16	17	18	19	20
21	22	23	24	25	26	27	28	29	30
31	32	33	34	35	36	37	38	39	40
41	42	43	44	45	46	47	48	49	50
51	52	53	54	55	56	57	58	59	60
61	62	63	64	65	66	67	68	69	70
71	72	73	74	75	76	77	78	79	80
81	82	83	84	85	86	87	88	89	90
91	92	93	94	95	96	97	98	99	100

Page 9 *(continued, top right)*

II
- **a** 14, 19, 24, 29
- **b** 32, 37, 42, 47
- **c** 53, 58, 63, 68
- **d** 28, 38, 48, 58,
- **e** 47, 57, 67, 77
- **f** 59, 69, 79, 89

Page 10

I
- **a** 5 cm
- **b** 6 cm
- **c** 8 cm
- **d** 2 cm
- **e** 10 cm
- **f** 11 cm

II about 1 metre – child
about 2 metres – door
about 10 cm – pencil
more than 2 metres – wall
about 50 cm – book

Page 11

I
- **a** 16
- **b** 16
- **c** 12
- **d** 18
- **e** 14
- **f** 19
- **g** 18
- **h** 14
- **i** 13

II
- **a** There are many possible solutions, check your child's additions total 13.
- **b** There are many possible solutions, check your child's additions total 18.

Page 12

I
- **a** 24
- **b** 40
- **c** 48
- **d** 62
- **e** 56
- **f** 37
- **g** 59
- **h** 31
- **i** 89
- **j** 93

II

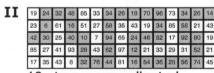

10 stars were collected.

Page 13

I

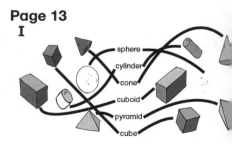

II
- **a** 2 square faces, 4 rectangle faces
- **b** 6 square faces
- **c** 1 square face, 4 triangle faces
- **d** 2 circle faces and a curved face